THE SUN is a GOLDEN EARRING

THE SUN is a GOLDEN EARRING

Natalia M. Belting
Illustrated by Bernarda Bryson

Holt, Rinehart and Winston / New York

BOOKS BY NATALIA BELTING

The Sun Is a Golden Earring
Elves and Ellefolk: *Tales of the Little People*
Indy and Mr. Lincoln
Verity Mullins and the Indian
Cat Tales

To Elizabeth Jean Hill— *a book for dreaming*

Before there were men, there was the sky and the sun and the moon and the stars. And when men came upon the earth, they looked at the sky and wondered. How came this blueness, and what had set alight the stars? Out of this wondering, they told tales.

They heard the thunder; it was as the beasts trumpeting in the jungle, as stones crashing down from the mountain. They beheld the lightning, and said among themselves, it is like the flash of the cord on a child's top; it is like the darting of a fish through the sea. It is like this and like that.

From forest clearings and ocean shores; in the warm hot lands of the south; in the cold dry lands of the north, east, and west; wherever men were, they looked at the sky, and some of them said: the sun is a golden earring; and some of them said: the stars are a woman's necklace.

Now read what they said, and consider. Behold how they pictured the sky, how they thought of the winds that blow through it, the storms that harass it. Then dream as they dreamed, and ponder, and match their thoughts to your own.

Some say the sun is a golden earring,
the earring of a beautiful girl.

A white bird took it from her
when she walked in the fields one day.
But it caught on a spider web
that stretches between the homes of men
and the homes of the gods.

—*from India*

The twilight clouds
are the clothes of the goddesses
hung out to air.

—*from India*

The moon is a white cat
that hunts
the gray mice of the night.

—*from Hungary*

The sun and the moon used to walk together,
until one day, when they walked
on a log across some mud
and the moon slipped off.
Her face was covered with mud.
The sun could not wait for her to wash her face.
He went ahead.
The moon is still trying to catch up with him,
and she still has a dirty face.

—from the Solomon Islands

Once, when the sky was very near the earth,
a woman hoeing in her garden took off her necklace
and hung it in the sky.
The stars are her silver necklace.

—from the Hawaiian Islands

The sky is a tent roof.
It is a tent roof stretched from a great post
that stands in the center of the world.
And the stars are holes in it that the winds blow through.

—from Siberia

The Milky Way is a long-stitched seam,
the seam where the skins of the sky are fastened together.
And the shooting stars are rays of light from the heavens,
when the gods pull the seam apart to look down on the earth.

—from Siberia

The Milky Way is the wild ducks' way,
the birds' road,
the way of the birds to the southland.

—from Estonia

The Milky Way is a sail,
the sail of a great canoe that goes among the stars.

—*from the Society Islands*

The Wind is a man with a spade in his hand.
He stands above the earth and shovels the winds.
He shovels the winds into the south,
and the winds that blow into the north.
He shovels the winds to the east and to the west.

—from Lapland

The winds dwell in the mountains,
and when the Changeable Wind blows,
the animals wake from their winter's sleep.
When the Blue Wind blows, the leaves come out.
When the Yellow Wind blows, the animals leave their dens
and the earth is covered with green, growing things.
When the Dark Wind blows, the snakes and the lizards
shed their winter-dry skins and put on fresh skins.

—from North America, Navaho Indians

The dark gray clouds,
the great gray clouds,
the black rolling clouds are elephants
going down to the sea for water.
They draw up the water in their trunks.
They march back again across the sky.
They spray the earth with the water,
and men say it is raining.

—from India

The high thin clouds are the stone pavements of the heavens.

—from the Marquis Islands

The storms are "running days,"
When the mountain spirit runs from mountain top to mountain top.

—from North America, Ute Indians

There are children who live beneath the earth.
They are like the children of the earth, but they live beneath it.
Their games are like the games of the children of the earth.
They play with balls and with darts and they spin tops.
And the lightning is the flash of the cords that sets their tops spinning.

—from Malaya

When the gods are angry,
they roll a stone across the floor of the heavens.
They roll the stone across the boards
that stretch from east to west across the skies.
They roll the stone across the boards
that stretch from north to south across the skies.
And men say it thunders.

—from India

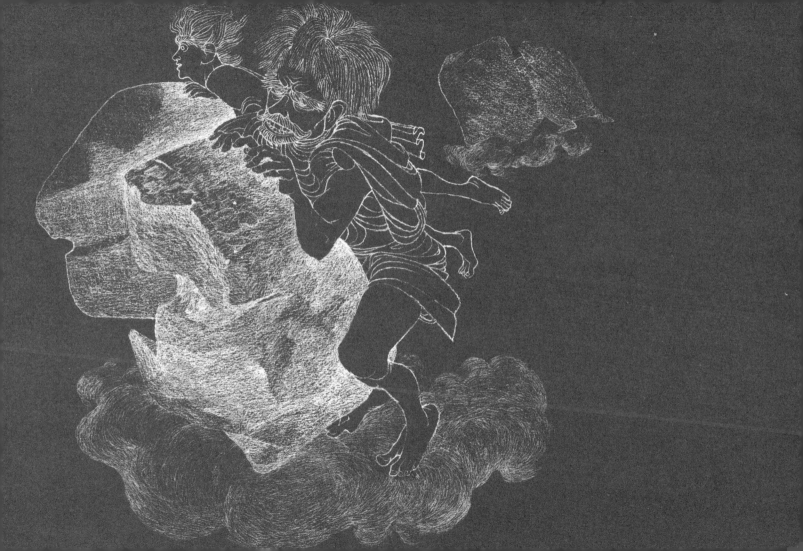

The thunder is a great dragon that lives in the water
and flies in the air.
He carries two stones.
When he strikes them together,
the lightning flashes and the thunder roars.
The dragon pursues the spirits of evil,
and wherever he finds them,
he slays them.
The evil spirits hide in the trees,
and the dragon destroys them.

—*from Mongolia*

When it storms,
a camel walks across the skies.
He has two riders.
One beats a drum. It is the thunder.
One waves a scarf. It is the lightning.

—*from Siberia*

An old woman lives in the sky.

She looks after the cows and the goats that belong to the gods.

She tethers the sheep to the rainbow.

She stakes out the sheep on the rainbow so they will not wander away.

—*from Siberia, the Kirghis*

The rainbow is the fishing line of the king of the dragons.
The king of the dragons sits in the high places above the earth,
in places where no man has ever been.
He fishes in the waters below the earth;
and the rainbow is his fishing line.

—*from Malaya*

The sun is a piece of rock crystal.

First Man fashioned it.

First Man chipped and smoothed and polished the crystal.

First Woman fastened white shells to the edge of it.

First Man made rays from sheet lightning and hung the sun in the sky.

The sun is a piece of rock crystal.

—from North America, Navaho Indians

The winds are made by great birds flapping their wings;
And the clouds are the wings of the birds hiding the light of the sky.

—*from North America, Chippewa Indians*

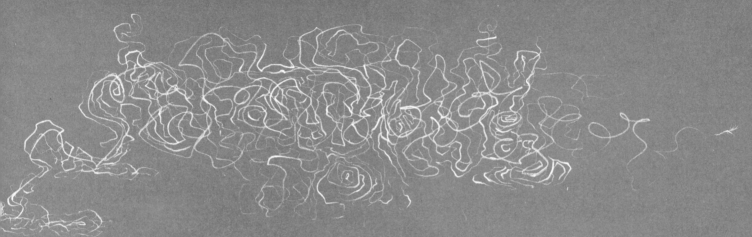

An old woman sat in front of her house one day, spinning.
The wind blew her thread and tangled it.
So the moon took pity on her and invited her to the sky:
invited her to live in the moon
where there is no wind.
The shadows on the moon are the old woman spinning
and her husband beside her smoking his long water pipe.

—from India

The stars are the jeweled pillars that hold up the sky
and make the house of the gods beautiful.

—*from Polynesia*

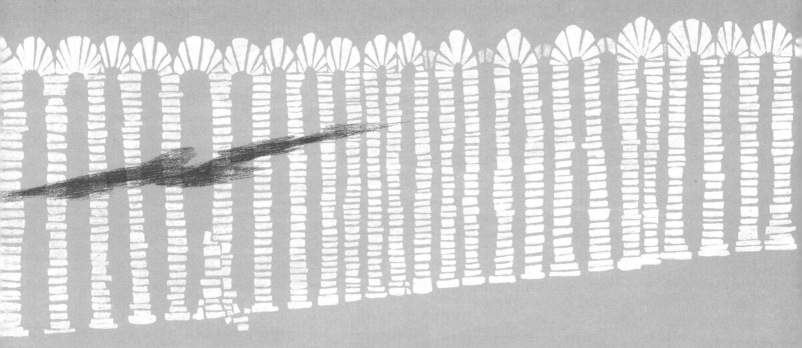

Some say the North Star is a nail on which the heavens are hung.

—*from Lapland*

NATALIA M. BELTING has received high praise for her folk tales, *Elves and Ellefolk* and *Cat Tales*. A professor of history at the University of Illinois, she specializes in the French colonization of North America and the ethnohistory of the Illinois Indians, whose ancient artifacts she excavates from her own land in Urbana.

BERNARDA BRYSON is as respected in the field of art and illustration as is her husband, Ben Shahn. In addition to having illustrated several children's books, including one of her own, her drawings appear in *Fortune* and *Scientific American*. Familiar with New Zealand, Southeast Asia, and Japan, and a frequent visitor to Europe, Miss Bryson is eminently qualified to illustrate a collection of folk sayings of the world.